Brain Waves

Vikings

Peter Hepplewhite
Neil Tonge

Folens Publishers

Editor: Michael Spilling
Illustrations: Gary Clifford–The Drawing Room

Layout artist: Suzanne Ward
Cover image: Fast Forward

© 1996 Folens Limited, on behalf of the authors.
Every effort has been made to contact copyright holders of material used in this book. If any have been overlooked, we will be pleased to make any necessary arrangements.
Reprinted 1998.
Reprinted 2000.

British Library Cataloguing in Publication Data. A catalogue record for this book is available from the British Library.

First published 1996 by Folens Limited, Dunstable and Dublin.
Folens Limited, Albert House, Apex Business Centre, Boscombe Road, Dunstable, LU5 4RL, England.

ISBN 1 85276 913-0

Contents

Introduction

The activity sheets in this book are designed to provide interesting and stimulating activities about the Vikings. The activities are grouped into three thematic areas:

- **Viking raids and settlement**, including their impact on the British Isles
- **everyday life**, including dwellings and home life, work and religion
- **the legacy of settlement**, including place names, myths and legends and Viking remains.

The activity sheets have been designed to be practical, interesting and visually stimulating. The sheets are intended to support existing resources and should be used in the context of broader classroom discussion of the topics concerned. In this way, the activity sheets could extend and develop certain aspects of historical enquiry for each topic. The topics do not need to be taught in sequence, but should be used selectively to stimulate, support and reinforce the teaching of history.

Each sheet has a specific focus within the topic concerned, and after a brief introduction the children are invited to explore a range of structured learning opportunities. These could be further developed in extension activities, such as classroom discussion, role play, and so on.

The questions and activities have been devised to:
- extend the children's knowledge and understanding of the issues introduced on the sheet within the context of the topic concerned
- assist the children in their understanding of history
- encourage the children to identify and use source material and to develop research skills.

The teachers' notes contain background information, along with ideas, suggestions and practical help. The notes include advice on potential pitfalls and problems, as well as details of materials required and ideas for extension activities.

Teachers' notes

Viking homelands   **page 9**

The so called 'Viking Age' began about AD800.
For three centuries the Norsemen (or Northmen)
of Norway, Sweden and Denmark dominated
much of northern Europe. They explored in
different directions: the Norwegians went west
to the British Isles, Iceland and Greenland; the
Danes went south-west to England, France and
northern Germany; and the Swedes went east
into Finland and Russia. Travel brochures could
provide useful classroom follow up: find out
about Scandinavians today and how they use
their Viking past to attract tourists.

The Vikings are coming   **page 10**

Geographers use 'push' and 'pull' factors to
explain movements of people. This exercise
introduces these terms while looking at the
reasons for the remarkable Viking expansion
from 800–1100. A growing population led to a
shortage of good land in a region of mountains
and poor soils, while technologically advanced
ships gave the adventurous the capability to
raid, trade or establish colonies. More able
children could discuss what personal motives
were likely to influence people to leave: for
example, first sons inherited land and property
so subsequent sons would have to make their
fortunes by other means.

The Viking world   **page 11**

Flat-bottomed, sturdy boats were the key to
Viking expansion. The voyages were splendid
achievements but must also have been great
feats of endurance. Discuss crossing the ocean in
boats only 23 metres by 5 metres with a crew of
about 60. Less able children could draw the
shape of a ship in the playground and sit in it.
More able children could discuss what they
would need to carry for the voyage, how they
might preserve food and what happens in a
storm. Enlarge the map to help less able children.

The Vikings in Britain   **page 12**

This activity encourages the children to
appreciate the scale of the Viking impact upon
Britain as a whole. This will help them to
consider the phases of invasion: from raids to
mass attacks to settlement and intermarriage.

Raid on Lindisfarne   **page 13**

Through primary sources the children learn of
the impact of early Viking raids and the
difficulty of interpretation of evidence. They
could attempt to complete two versions of the
same event to consider differing points of view.

England divided 1 and 2   **pages 14–15**

In the ninth century the kingdoms of Saxon
England were hit by a Viking whirlwind.
Within 10 years they had all been conquered
except Wessex. Alfred's achievement was to
rally this last Saxon kingdom and confine the
Viking advance to the Danelaw boundary. It is
important to remember that he was not King of
England and would not have been recognised as
such by the peoples of the other kingdoms.
Over the course of time, the Vikings settled in
England and had a profound influence on the
language and customs of the north and east of
the country. Read the children extracts from
The Anglo-Saxon Chronicle, a history of this
period written by Anglo-Saxon monks. More
able children could investigate this chronicle
for themselves.

Choose your Viking weapons   **page 16**

A weapon was a precious object, handed down
from father to son. It would take a smith many
hours to heat and reheat, twist and beat a sword
blade to the right strength and shape. When a
king raised an army he expected his warriors to
assemble fed, washed and armed ready for
battle. The most feared soldiers were the
berserkers who fought in a mad rage, possibly
induced by drugs. Discuss the advantages and
disadvantages of each weapon shown. Ask the
children to think about the kind of names given
to types of weapons now, such as the Tornado
fighter plane and Challenger tank. Why choose
names like this? How is this similar to the kind
of names Vikings used?

Building a Viking ship   **page 17**

Building a ship required skilled craftspeople.
This activity helps the children to understand
the range of craftspeople and the types of tools
they used, and also develop their decision-
making skills.

Teachers' notes

Viking longship   **page 18**

The Viking longship was a superb example of Viking craftsmanship. In this exercise the children will develop their historical vocabulary by learning the correct terms for parts of the boat and some of the crew members.

Dragon ship   **page 19**

Vikings loved their boats and lavished attention on them. A good shipwright was an asset to any community. Most boats had plain prows but archaeological and written evidence suggest that dragon's heads were also used. Look out for photographs of replica ships with dragon's heads, such as *The Viking* built in Norway in 1893 or *Odin's Raven* built on the Isle of Man in 1979. Both ships undertook long voyages and were very seaworthy, even in rough conditions.

Viking trader   **pages 20–21**

The Vikings were superb sailors and reached many uncharted parts of the known world. This activity helps the children to learn about the countries the Vikings reached and the extent of their trading connections. The children will have to make careful decisions by keeping a trading log.

Finding your way at sea   **page 22**

Despite the lack of sophisticated navigational instruments, the Vikings made amazing journeys across uncharted oceans. This activity will enable the children to follow instructions and appreciate the skill of Viking seamanship. They will eventually arrive in Greenland.

Advising Ethelred   **page 23**

Ethelred became king in 978 when he was only 11 years old. The Vikings attacked England in ever-increasing numbers and Ethelred was faced with difficult decisions. This activity encourages the children to think about the advantages and disadvantages of particular courses of action facing the Anglo-Saxon defenders. This could be a group activity, where each group represents the members of the King's council. In reality Ethelred paid Danegeld, which only succeeded in attracting future attacks. The whole class could discuss the possible courses of action.

Viking raiding camp   **page 24**

The Vikings escalated attacks on Britain from summer raiding parties to armies that wintered in England. In this instance, the children have to put themselves in the place of the Vikings and make decisions based on this knowledge. This page could be enlarged to A3 size.

The last Viking invasion   **page 25**

This activity introduces the children to one of the lasting impacts of the Vikings on England and encourages them to interpret evidence associated with the invasion.

Build a Viking house   **page 26**

In this activity the children develop an understanding of the construction of Viking homes and an appreciation of why particular materials were used. Only basic instructions are given in order to allow for variations depending on materials available.

Inside a Viking home   **page 27**

Most Viking families lived in rural longhouses, often one big room for the people and another for the animals. Sometimes there were extra facilities. Ash from a volcano preserved a fine Viking home at Stong in Iceland. This had a separate hall, living room, dairy and toilet. Town houses followed a similar pattern, usually with a workshop or warehouse attached. Discuss the problems of an extended family, say six people from three generations, living, playing, cooking, eating and sleeping in one room. Make a list of the advantages and disadvantages.

Cooking   **page 28**

Some background research might be necessary before doing this activity. Impress on the children that food was precious and rarely wasted. A bad harvest or a long winter brought the risk of starvation. Discuss the kinds of cooking it would be difficult to do without an oven. Think about the problems encountered when storing and preserving foods in a time before fridges: fish and meat could be dried and fruits and vegetables pickled. Point out that certain common modern foods such as potatoes, rice and pasta were unknown.

Teachers' notes

Viking women   **page 29**
Viking women appear to have had near equality and a good deal of personal freedom. They could choose and divorce a husband, run a business and own property. Clothing conventions indicated a woman's status. Unmarried and widowed women had long uncovered hair while married women wore an embroidered white scarf. Discuss what kind of husband a Viking woman might want: a good trader, farmer, or warrior, who was hard-working, kind, perhaps from a family who were friends of her family.

Clean or dirty?   **page 30**
These sources present the children with primary but contradictory sources about the Vikings. The children have the problem of interpreting evidence and possible explanations as to why the sources differ. Indicate to the children that the first group of Vikings were travelling merchants.

Pastimes   **page 31**
In the first game the rules are supplied for the children to follow. In the second they have to devise a system for playing the game.

Industries   **page 32**
Excavations at the Viking town of Hedeby in Denmark have pieced together a picture of a busy trading city with workshops belonging to craftspeople including potters, cobblers, metalworkers, jewellers, ivory and antler carvers and soapstone workers. Use text books to make a classroom frieze of a busy crafts and shopping area.

Artefacts   **page 33**
Viking material culture was largely self-sufficient, animals and natural resources providing for most needs. The women of the household made most of the clothes from wool or linen, working the raw material into the finished product. Other items, such as shoes, might be bought from craftspeople. Scandinavian products such as amber, furs, walrus tusks and deer antlers were traded for luxuries such as glassware, jewellery and silk. Compare everyday household objects today.

How many are made from 'natural' resources and how many from complex industrial processes? How many could we make for ourselves?

Sacrifice   **page 34**
Ibn Fadlan was an Arab diplomat from the Caliph of Baghdad to the Rus of the middle Volga. The Rus are thought to be Swedish Vikings settled in Russia. This source is rather controversial because there are no other descriptions of such gruesome ceremonies in Viking literature. Slaves or 'thralls' were at the bottom of Viking society, doing most of the menial work. Discuss the idea of slavery. Ask the children what it would feel like to be owned by someone else and have to do as they say. It is possible that the girl felt she was being given a great honour that she eagerly accepted.

Names   **page 35**
This fun sheet introduces the subject of nicknames and why people use them. Make a display of photographs and nicknames for politicians, sports and media personalities.

Crime and punishment   **page 36**
All societies are faced with the problem of how they enforce the law. This will help the children to understand some of the difficulties of enforcing the law in Viking society.

In memory   **page 37**
This activity introduces the children to further types of evidence that tell us about the Vikings. The children are also faced with the difficulties of interpretation.

Runes   **page 38**
In this activity the children use Viking runic writing to find the correct craftspeople. They also consolidate their understanding of the types of craftspeople needed in Viking society. The missing name is 'boatmaker'.

Who goes where?   **page 39**
These Viking sources show the different ranks in Viking society. The children have to interpret the sources and assign the correct description.

Teachers' notes

Heroes   **page 40**
This source illustrates what Vikings thought about their heroes. The children should be encouraged to think about what constitutes heroes and how this determines a particular interpretation of the past.

Making Thor's hammer   **page 41**
Thor was second in importance only to Odin. More able children could research Viking craftsmanship and the importance of superstitious belief. Less able children could make a simple amulet from modelling clay.

Advice from Odin   **page 42**
These Viking proverbs were passed down for generations by word of mouth before they were eventually written down. Discuss with the children what they can tell us about Viking life, such as the need to be on guard against enemies. Compare this ancient advice with proverbs we use today or sayings used in the children's families.

Reading the stones   **page 43**
The Viking Age has left a rich collection of stone sculpture. The famous Ragnarok Stone (or Cross from Kirk Andreas) on the Isle of Man shows that traditional Viking beliefs coexisted with their conversion to Christianity. Some scholars have interpreted the Cross as the triumph of Christianity (Christ survives while Odin dies); others think that the sculptor was simply pointing out similarities and contrasts between Christian and Viking theologies. More able children could be asked to draw the missing parts of the Stone using stories from the Bible and Viking mythology.

Burial   **page 44**
In this activity the children have to analyse the nature of evidence and attempt to form a hypothesis about the individual in the grave.

Digging up the Vikings   **page 45**
Much of our information about the Vikings comes from written sources. The Icelandic sagas record a vivid and larger-than-life picture of Viking adventures. The work of archaeologists has been vital in adding to this. Famous digs include Yorvik (York) in England and Hedeby in Germany. A fun classroom task showing the principles of archaeology could include burying objects in a sand tray for the children to excavate. Broken pots, bones and reproduction artefacts could be hidden. Use tools such as fine brushes, riddles and trowels. Categorise and draw conclusions about the finds, such as what kind of animals were kept.

Festival   **page 46**
The Up-Helly-Aa festival is not an ancient custom, but a Victorian revival. However, it has lasted over a hundred years and is now accepted as a genuine folk custom. Activities for a school Viking day might include making cardboard helmets, shields and swords, preparing unleavened bread and a vegetable stew (no potatoes), storytelling or learning passages from the sagas, and holding a Viking fair selling items such as honey cakes, leather goods and bead necklaces.

Viking English   **page 47**
Old English and Norse were similar languages, both derived from Old German.

		Viking or Old Norse	Anglo-Saxon or Old English
rear	raise	*raise*	*rear*
wish	want	*want*	*wish*
skill	craft	*skill*	*craft*
hide	skin	*skin*	*hide*
scant	short	*scant*	*short*

The children need to use a good dictionary that shows the origins of words, such as the *Collins School Dictionary*.

The Vikings settled here   **page 48**
Place names can provide useful evidence about early settlement. *The Concise Oxford Dictionary of English Place Names* is an excellent classroom tool for expanding this exercise, looking at the full meaning of local names. More able children could begin to use more detailed maps, including the Ordnance Survey. Remember that in some areas Celtic, Roman or French names may predominate.

Viking homelands

The Vikings came from Norway, Sweden and Denmark in Scandinavia. This jigsaw map shows their homelands.

● Cut out the pieces and glue them together correctly.
● Finish the names of the countries and use an atlas to help you label the seas.

Your map shows Scandinavia in Viking times.

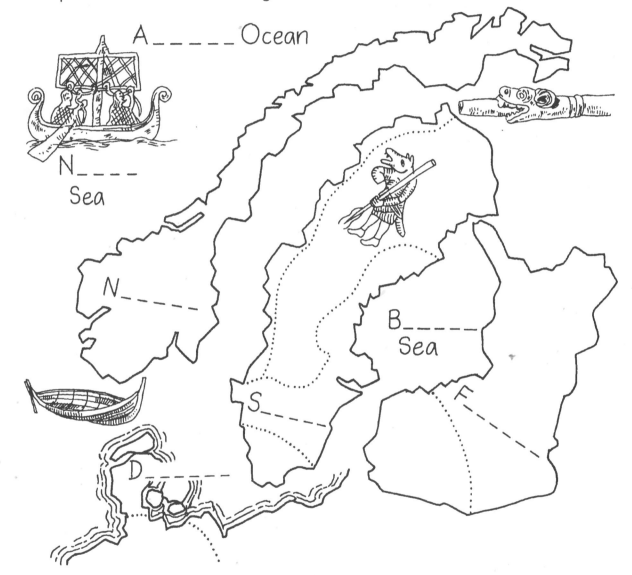

A _ _ _ _ _ Ocean

N_ _ _ _
Sea

N _ _ _ _

B _ _ _ _
Sea

S _ _

F

D _ _ _ _ _ _

● Use an atlas to draw a modern map of Scandinavia, including all the borders of the countries.
● What are the differences between Scandinavia today and Scandinavia in Viking times?
● Which Scandinavian country was not Viking?

The Vikings are coming

The Vikings left their homelands for several reasons. Some things 'pushed' or forced them to go, while other things 'pulled' or attracted them to new lands.

● Cut out the labels and match them with the correct picture.
● Tick the boxes if you think it is a 'push' reason. Put a cross in the box if you think it is a 'pull' reason.

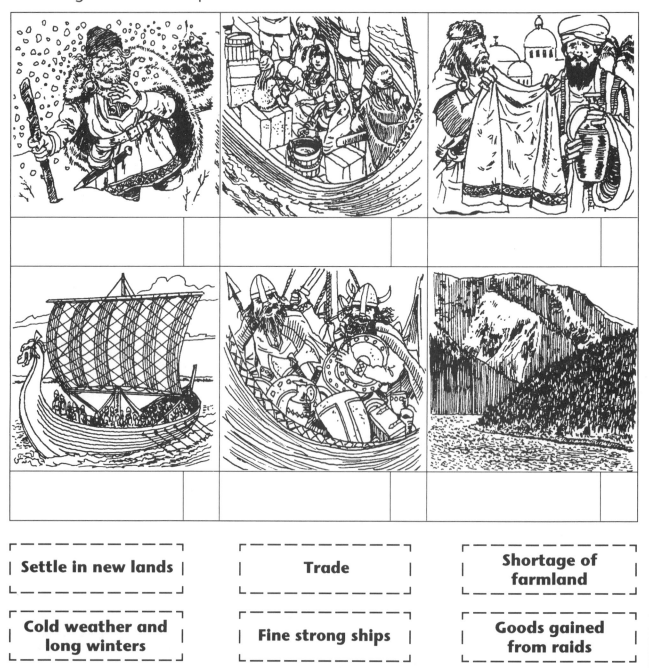

┌ ─ ─ ─ ─ ─ ─ ─ ─ ─ ┐   ┌ ─ ─ ─ ─ ─ ─ ─ ─ ─ ┐   ┌ ─ ─ ─ ─ ─ ─ ─ ─ ─ ┐
│ **Settle in new lands** │   │   **Trade**   │   │   **Shortage of**   │
│   │   │   │   │   **farmland**   │
└ ─ ─ ─ ─ ─ ─ ─ ─ ─ ┘   └ ─ ─ ─ ─ ─ ─ ─ ─ ─ ┘   └ ─ ─ ─ ─ ─ ─ ─ ─ ─ ┘

┌ ─ ─ ─ ─ ─ ─ ─ ─ ─ ┐   ┌ ─ ─ ─ ─ ─ ─ ─ ─ ─ ┐   ┌ ─ ─ ─ ─ ─ ─ ─ ─ ─ ┐
│ **Cold weather and** │   │ **Fine strong ships** │   │   **Goods gained** │
│   **long winters**   │   │   │   │   **from raids**   │
└ ─ ─ ─ ─ ─ ─ ─ ─ ─ ┘   └ ─ ─ ─ ─ ─ ─ ─ ─ ─ ┘   └ ─ ─ ─ ─ ─ ─ ─ ─ ─ ┘

● List the pictures in order of importance.
● Explain your reasons for the order you have chosen.

BRAIN WAVES – *Vikings*

The Viking world

The Vikings criss-crossed half the world in their longships.
They were great explorers and traders. Help them find their way.

- Using an atlas, fill in the names of these rivers:
  Rhine, Danube, Dnieper, Volga.

- Find the names of these places:
  Oslo, Yorvik, London, Dublin, Paris, Rome, Constantinople,
  Baghdad, Novgorod, Bulgar, Alexandria, Iceland, Newfoundland.

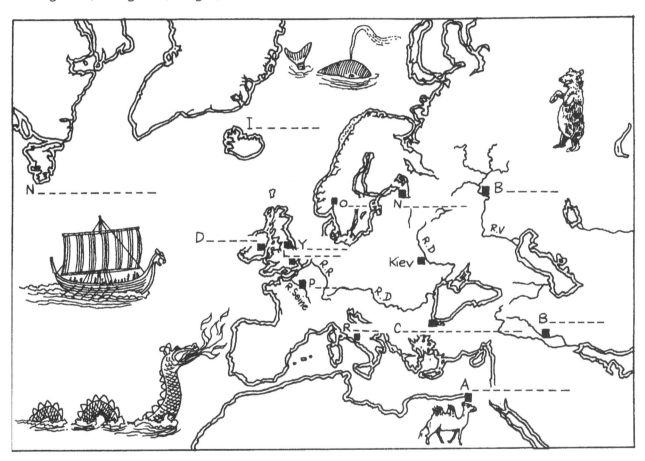

- Starting from Oslo, neatly draw in red the route you would
  take by sea to reach the following:
  - London
  - Rome
  - Newfoundland. (This is a long journey – you need to make it
    in three or four shorter hops. Where would you rest?)

   - Mark the shortest route, using seas and rivers, to:
  - Constantinople
  - Baghdad.

The Vikings in Britain

● Draw a line to join each box to the correct place on the map.

The Isle of Man
The Isle of Man is in the middle of the Irish Sea and made a good base to raid nearby countries. On the island, archaeologists have found the grave of a chieftain buried in a boat with his weapons.

Scotland
Raiding parties sailed toward Scotland. The monastery at Iona came under attack in AD795, 802 and 806. The monks fled to Ireland.

Some Viking crews reached the mainland and settled there to farm the land. Some sent for their families to join them. Others married the local people, called the Picts. After a time the two people forget their differences. Even the royal families of Scotland and Norway were joined by marriage.

Ireland
In the eighth century, Ireland was a rich country. It was divided into several kingdoms but they came under one leader called the High King. Irish monasteries were famous as places of learning and great wealth. They became a target for the Viking raids.

In 839 the Vikings attacked in large numbers. They built camps called longphorts, which grew into Ireland's first cities: Dublin, Wexford, Waterford and Cork. Many Vikings came to Ireland and settled in the towns or became farmers.

Wales
In the ninth century, Vikings attacked Wales. During one raid they took 2000 slaves.

Some Vikings settled in Wales and were gradually accepted by the Welsh people. Viking traders gave Scandinavian names to areas along the Welsh coast, such as Steephom, Stokhom and Flathom.

● What kind of places did the Vikings attack first?
● Why did they choose these sorts of places to attack?
● Why do you think the Vikings stopped raiding and settled down?

   ● Did the Vikings come to the part of Britain where you live? What local evidence is there?

Raid on Lindisfarne

In the year 793 the small island of Lindisfarne in Northumberland was attacked by Vikings. It was one of the first raids on England. There was a monastery at Lindisfarne which probably attracted the Viking raiders. This is how the Saxons wrote about the raids.

In the year 793 terrible signs appeared in the sky over Northumbria which frightened the people. There were whirlwinds and flashes of lightning and fiery dragons were seen in the air. All the crops failed and so there was nothing to eat. Then the heathens came and destroyed God's church on Lindisfarne.

Anglo-Saxon Chronicle, 890

The Viking raiders came like stinging hornets, from all sides like wolves. They robbed and slaughtered not only sheep and oxen, but even priests, monks and nuns.

Simeon of Durham, in the 1100s

- When were these accounts written?

  Anglo-Saxon chronicle _____

  Simeon of Durham _____

- These accounts were written many years after the raid. How do you think the authors knew what to write?
- Who wrote these accounts? Do you think they are describing what really happened?
- The first piece of writing tells us terrible things happened before the Vikings came. What were they? Do you think they are true? Why?

- With a partner, write two accounts of the raid. One of you should write from the Anglo-Saxon point of view, and the other from the Viking point of view.
- Compare your accounts.

England divided 1

In the ninth century, the Vikings almost conquered Britain.
These cards show what happened.

● Cut out the boxes and arrange them in the correct order to make a timeline.

In 870 the Vikings attacked East Anglia and killed King Edmund. King Burgred of Mercia tried to save his kingdom by paying the Vikings not to attack. They took his money but still invaded. In 874 Mercia fell to the Vikings. Only Wessex remained unconquered.

In May 876 Alfred gathered a new army. He beat the Viking leader Guthrum at the Battle of Edington. They made a peace treaty and England was split in two. The Viking lands became known as the Danelaw.

In 865 the Vikings came to stay. The Great Army landed in East Anglia and began to attack the kingdoms of England one by one. In 866 they captured York and in 867 they killed Aella of Northumbria.

After 880 Alfred made Wessex strong to fight off new Viking attacks. Towns were built with strong walls. English armies trained to fight all year round. Large ships were built to catch Viking raiders out at sea.

Wessex was ruled by a young king, Alfred. In 878 he was caught by surprise. The Viking leader Guthrum attacked just after Christmas, when the English army was at home. Alfred barely escaped and hid in the marshes of Somerset.

The first Viking raid on England was in 793 with a shocking attack on the monks of Lindesfarne.

● Using the headlines, match the correct words for five of the cards.
● Make up the missing one yourself.

Monks Flee Viking Horror

East Anglia and Mercia Down

Surprise Christmas Attack

Great Army here to Stay

Vikings Agree to Danelaw

England divided 2

- Cut out the pictures and match them with the
  written cards on page 14.

- Write the date on each picture card.
- Draw a picture on the blank card to show
  a scene to match the written card.

- Find out which other countries the Vikings invaded.
  Use **The Viking World** (page 11) and reference books to help you.

Choose your Viking weapons

Weapons were very expensive in Viking times, especially those made of iron. Weapons would be handed down from father to son, as if they were precious jewellery. A sword or axe might be given a name like *Odin's Fire* or *Skull Splitter*.

Imagine you are a young but poor Viking warrior. The chief has agreed to loan you some weapons for your first raid.

● Choose three weapons.

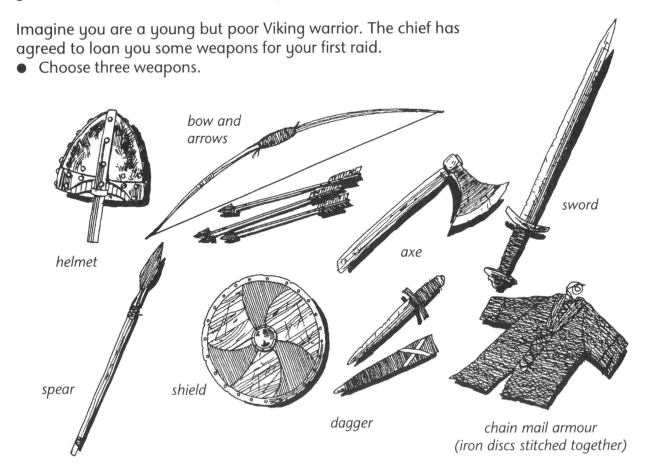

bow and arrows

helmet

spear

shield

axe

dagger

sword

chain mail armour
(iron discs stitched together)

● Give reasons for your choice.

I would choose	My reason is
1.	
2.	
3.	

● Draw a picture of yourself wearing or holding these weapons and armour. Give your weapons some fierce names.

Building a Viking ship

Snorri Storlson is about to build a ship. He is a shipwright.
All the tools have been mixed up. Each of Snorri's workers
needs the right tool.

- Draw a line to join the craftspeople to the tool he or she
  needs to build the ship.

Olaf He hammers the nails into
the planks of wood.

Frer She twists the seal
skin into ropes.

Vigdis She weaves the cloth
to make the sails.

Magnus He cuts the
wood for the boat.

Sven He shapes the wood
for the ship.

Knut He makes the nails
to keep the planks of the
ship together.

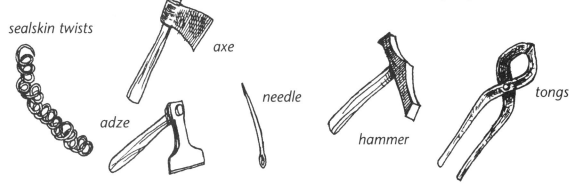

sealskin twists   *axe*   *adze*   *needle*   *hammer*   *tongs*

- Use the information to draw a series of pictures to show how the ship
  was built. Add captions to explain what is happening.
- In groups, mime the different jobs that are needed to build the ship.

Viking longship

Snorri Storlson has all the pieces to put a Viking Longship together.
Can you help him?

● Cut out the pieces and stick them on a new sheet of paper to make a longship.

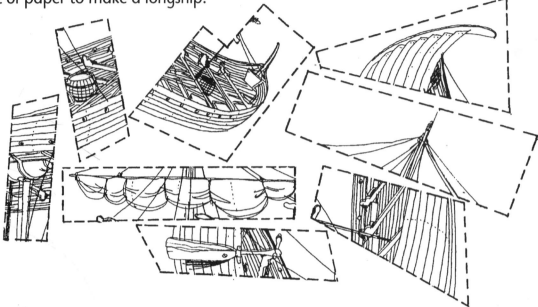

● Where will these names go? Cut out these labels and stick them in place.

Prow: the front of the ship

Stern: the back of the ship

Rudder: a large paddle to steer the ship

Mast: large pole for the sail

Sail: large sheet

Seaman's Chest: water barrel

● Where will the Viking sailors go?

Eric steers the boat.

Harold looks after the sails.

Olaf is a lookout at the front of the boat.

● What will you call your ship? The Vikings liked fierce names that would frighten their enemies, like *Sea Wolf*.

Dragon ship

Viking ships often had their prows (front ends) carved in the shape of a dragon's head. Their sails were often painted to look like wings. They did this to frighten their enemies and scare away evil spirits.

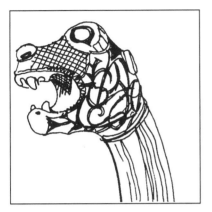 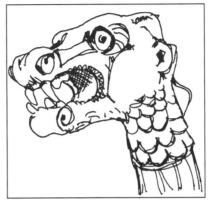 

● Draw your own dragon's head.

Vikings gave their ships exciting names like *Long Serpent* or *Raven of the Wind*.

● Give your ship a name and write a poem about it battling through a stormy sea.

● This Viking poem might help:
The arms of men from Norway are driving
This iron-studded dragon
Down the storm-tossed river,
Like an eagle with wings beating.

Viking trader – game

How to play

You are one of four Viking traders:

Sven
Olaf
Harald
Knut

You live in Yorvik. Decide where you are going to make your trading voyage. Decide on a time limit for the game before you begin, for example, 15 or 20 minutes. You must keep exactly to the time.

What to do

1. Using the map, you can visit as many places as you want, but remember the game must end at the time you have all agreed.
2. You have 30 gold pieces to spend on your trading voyage. The price of goods is shown in the key.
3. Keep a trading log of your journey.
4. Roll a six-sided dice. Move the number of spaces.
5. The game ends when the time is finished. The winner is the trader who is closest to home and has bought the most goods. If you have managed to arrive back in Yorvik or are one space away then you get the full amount. If you are two spaces away take two off your total, if three spaces away then take off three, and so on.

Trading log		
Place visited	**Goods bought**	**Price**

End of game
Price of goods bought
(less number of spaces from home).

Total _____

BRAIN WAVES – *Vikings*

Viking trader – map

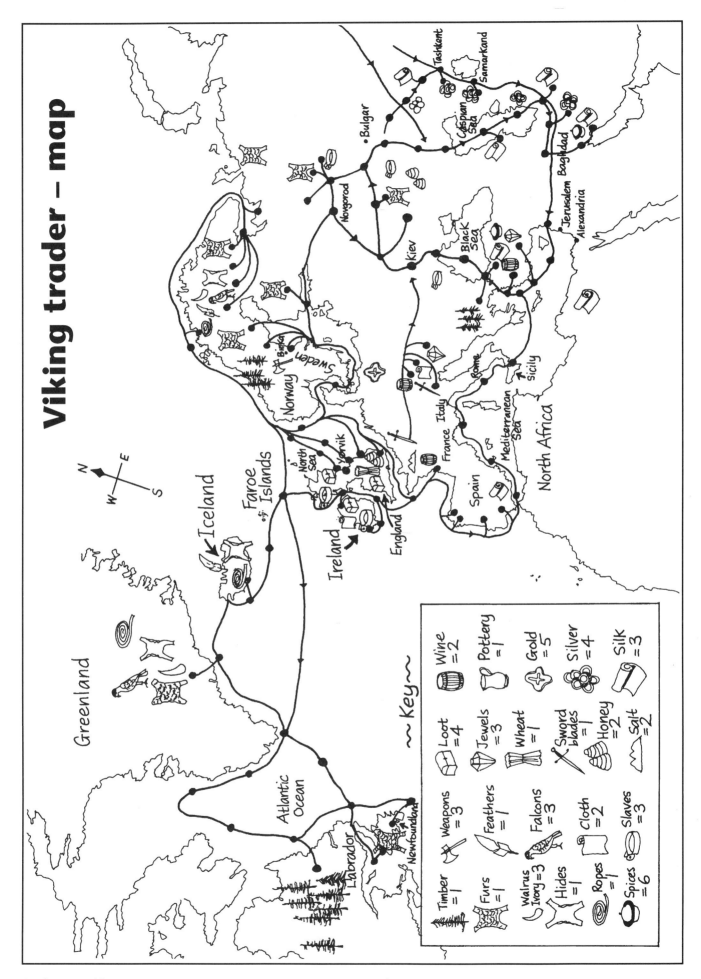

Finding your way at sea

The Vikings were skilful sailors who made sea voyages of thousands of miles. They did all this without a magnetic compass. How did they do it?

This is a map and some instructions the Vikings might have used to find their way at sea. Follow the directions and find out where they sailed.

1. Leave Yorvik and keep the pole star ahead of you.
   The pole star is always to the north in the night sky.
2. There will be an island blown by cold winds.
3. The sun will rise to the east each day. Make sure you sail in the opposite direction to the waking sun and to the left of the pole star.
4. You will arrive at a land of volcanoes and hot springs.
5. Sail once more away from the rising sun straight as an arrow.
6. Puffins and guillemots will tell you that you are not far from land. Near the coast you will see thick clouds. Whales will be close to the shore.

● Where are you? _____

● Other Viking routes are marked on the map. Use the points of the compass to direct your partner along a Viking route. For example, two squares east, one square south and so on.

Advising Ethelred

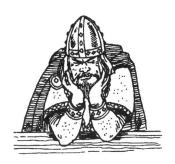

King Ethelred is not sure what to do. The Vikings are attacking England. You are his chief adviser.

● Write what you think about these ideas.

	Good points	Bad points
Pay the Vikings Danegeld (Dane's Gold) to go away.		
Fight and stand up to the Vikings.		
Pray to God for help against the Vikings.		
Make the towns stronger.		
Bribe some Vikings to fight for King Ethelred.		
Build ships to fight the Vikings at sea.		

NOW ● What would you tell Ethelred to do? Why?

_____

_____

_____

continue on the other side

Viking raiding camp

In 850 a large Viking army came to England. They decided to stay the winter and raid again the following summer. They needed to build a camp that would be safe from attack and be easy to supply.

- On the picture there are five possible sites. In the box below, explain the advantages and disadvantages of each.
- Which site is the best? Explain your choice.

Site	Advantages	Disadvantages	Mark out of 10
Thanet Island			
Rocky Bay			
Gentle Hills			
Lake Waite			
Steep Hills			

Steep Hills

Rocky Bay

Woodland

Gentle Hills

North Sea

Moorland

Steep Cliffs

Ford (crossing place)

From Denmark

Thanet Island

Woodland

Marshy Ground

Lake Waite

0 miles 5

NOW In 865 an even larger Danish army arrived. This time many of the Vikings decided to stay.

- Which site would they choose now for a farming settlement?

BRAIN WAVES – *Vikings* © Folens (copiable page)

The last Viking invasion

This is a picture taken from the famous Bayeux Tapestry. It tells the story of William of Normandy's invasion of England. He defeated the English king, Harold.

- What does the picture show?
- How can you tell these ships are invading?
- Do you think that this picture shows all of the Viking ships, or just some of them? Explain your answer.
- Why do you think William needed many ships for his invasion?

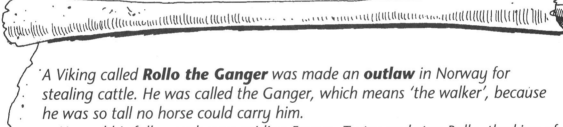

*A Viking called **Rollo the Ganger** was made an **outlaw** in Norway for stealing cattle. He was called the Ganger, which means 'the walker', because he was so tall no horse could carry him.*

*He and his followers began raiding France. To try and stop Rollo, the king of France gave him Normandy, a part of north-west France, to rule over in 927. The French called the men from Norway '**Northmen'**. Over many years this came to be shortened to '**Normans'**.*

*In 1066 England was invaded and conquered by Normans led by **William, Duke of Normandy**. William was an **ancestor** of Rollo.*

- Tell the story in pictures, like the Bayeux Tapestry.
- Choose how many pictures you will need to tell the story. Underneath each picture write a short description of what is happening in the picture.
- Look up the words printed in bold.

Build a Viking house

This is a model of a Viking house discovered in Iceland. Iceland is a very cold country, so Viking houses needed very thick walls that were windproof and waterproof.

To make the model:
1. Use a hardboard or very thick card base about 20cm x 30cm.
2. Draw the outline of the house on the hardboard.
3. Place gravel around the outline of the house and cover the gravel with strong glue.
4. Make the walls of the house with strips of card. Draw lines on the card to make it look like wooden planking.
5. Cut out one end of the house so that you can see inside the building.
6. Use dowelling to make the framework of the house.
7. Use card and layers of papier maché to build up the turf walls. Paint these green to look like turf.
8. You could make a hearth, platform seats and a long trestle table from card.

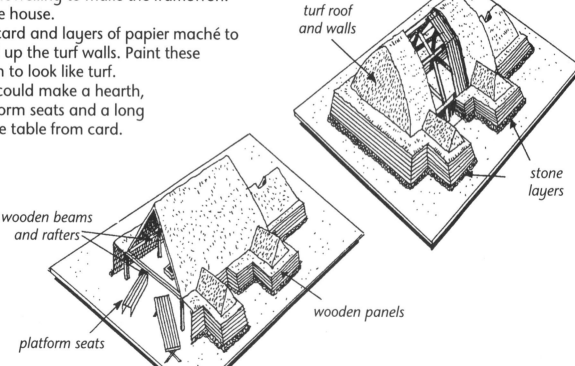

ground plan

hardboard base

turf roof and walls

stone layers

wooden beams and rafters

platform seats

wooden panels

- Write about how Viking houses in Iceland looked and why they were built in this way.
- You could make more model houses in your class and put them together to make a model Viking settlement.

Inside a Viking home

Most Vikings lived in farmhouses in the countryside. Usually everybody lived in one large room. This picture is based on evidence found by archaeologists.

● Draw a line from each box to the correct part of the picture.

| loom for making cloth |
| iron cooking pot hanging from roof |
| wooden food tubs |
| open fire on clay hearth |
| carved wooden bed |

| bench with sheepskin cover |
| wooden bowls for eating |
| clothes chest |
| broom |
| clay platforms for sleeping and sitting on |

● How do you think the artist knew what to draw?
● What evidence do you think the artist might have used?
● Do you think this is a true picture of a Viking home?

 ● Make a chart to compare Viking objects with objects in your home.

Objects in a Viking house	Objects in my home
iron cooking pot	
open fire on clay hearth	
clothes chest	
broom	
bench with sheepskin cover	

Cooking

Cooking was usually done by women and girls, using an open fire. This woman has her fire burning brightly and her kitchen tools ready.

● Write in the table the kind of cooking she might do with each tool (such as roasting) and a food that could be cooked like this.

Kitchen tool	Cooking method	Food
Iron cauldron		
Shallow iron pan		
Iron spit		
Iron fork		

● In what ways is this the same as cooking today?

● Look at this list of ingredients. Write a recipe for a meal a Viking woman could make for her family. (She might not use all of them.)

● Describe how she might cook the meal.

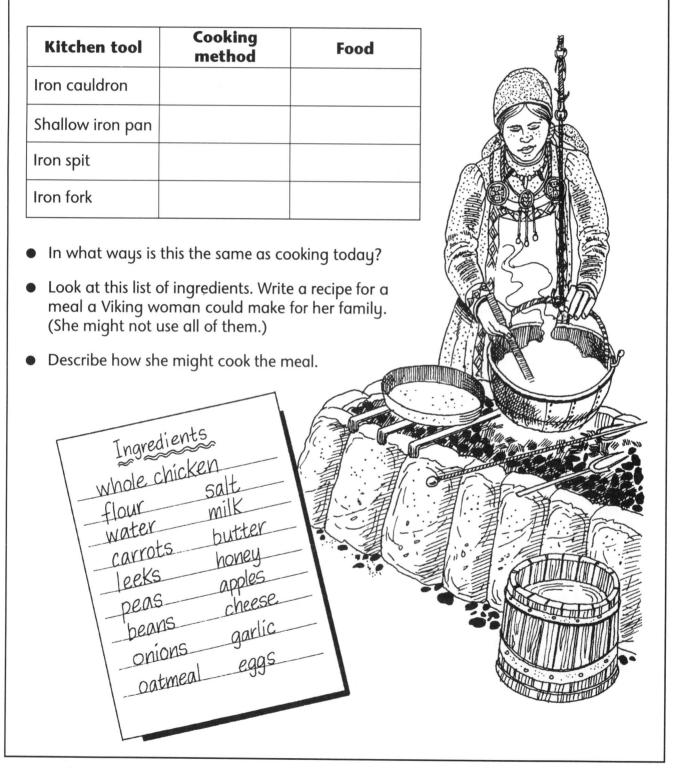

Ingredients

whole chicken
flour   salt
water   milk
carrots   butter
leeks   honey
peas   apples
beans   cheese
onions   garlic
oatmeal   eggs

Viking women

Viking women were independent and hard-working. Look at this list of activities they might have done, some once or twice in their lives, some every day.

● Write them out under the correct heading shown below.

make butter
move with husband to new country
preserve meat with salt
clean house
pickle vegetables in vinegar
collect sheep's wool
spin wool
raise children
weave wool to make cloth
make clothes
grind grain to make flour

choose a husband or stay single
defend farm when husband is away
preserve animal skins to make leather
use leather to make shoes, coats and hats
learn family history
slaughter animals
comb wool
divorce husband if unhappy
prepare meals
be in charge of slaves
milk cows and goats
dry fish

Farming	Running a family	Clothing a family	Feeding a family	Other jobs

● Which do think were the hardest jobs?
● Choose five of the things that a woman today would not have to do. Explain why.

Clean or dirty?

These are two pieces of evidence that tell us about the personal habits of the Vikings.

On a journey to Russia in 921 an Arab trader came across a band of Viking warrior-merchants.

> *They are the filthiest of God's creatures. They do not wash after going to the toilet nor before and after meals. Every day they wash their faces and heads in the same water. This is how it is done. Every morning a slave girl brings her master a large bowl of water in which he washes his face and hands and hair, combing it also over the bowl. He then blows his nose and spits into the water. When he has finished the slave girl then takes the bowl to his neighbour – until the bowl has gone round twenty or thirty people. All have blown their noses, spat, and washed their faces and hair in the water.*

> *They combed their hair most carefully, had a bath on Saturdays and changed their underclothes often.*

An English writer of the same time had a different opinion.

- Write one point in each box that is not very healthy.
- Why might there be two different descriptions of how the Vikings kept clean?
- Does this mean that one of the writers was not telling the truth? Explain your answer.

Pastimes

During the long winter months there might be only three or four hours of daylight and snow all around. Chess was a favourite game. *Hnefetafl* was another game popular with the Vikings.

RULES FOR HNEFETAFL
Preparation

There are white pieces and black pieces. Each player has twelve pieces. There is one extra black piece that is bigger than the rest. This is the king. The Vikings often used different coloured pebbles as pieces. The king is in the centre of the board surrounded by the other black pieces. The white pieces are placed on the squares around the outside of the board, three on each edge. The object of the game is for the king to reach one of the corners.

Rules

- Each player moves one piece one square at a time, taking turns. The pieces cannot move diagonally.
- If a piece has two pieces of the other colour on two sides then it is taken off the board.
- The white pieces cannot use the three squares in each corner.

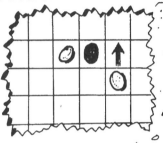

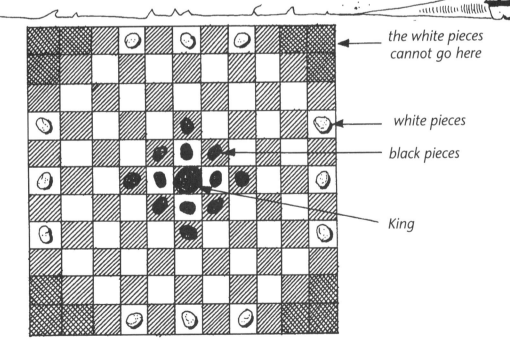

the white pieces cannot go here

white pieces

black pieces

King

- Your Viking chief asks you to make a new game using the same board and pieces. Invent some rules for your new game and try them out.

Industries

- Match the craftsperson with the picture.
- Write what each person is doing.

I am a _____

My job today is _____

I am a _____

My job today is _____

I am a _____

My job today is _____

I am a _____

My job today is _____

- Make a list of things a Viking could buy from these people.
- Which of these jobs do you think was the most important? Why?
- Are jobs like this still done today? Choose one and explain how it is the same as or different to the Viking job.

Artefacts

An artefact is an object made by someone using raw materials.
When the Vikings made things they often used parts of animals they farmed or hunted.

- Look at the pictures below. Fill in the table by matching the artefact with the correct raw material and animal.

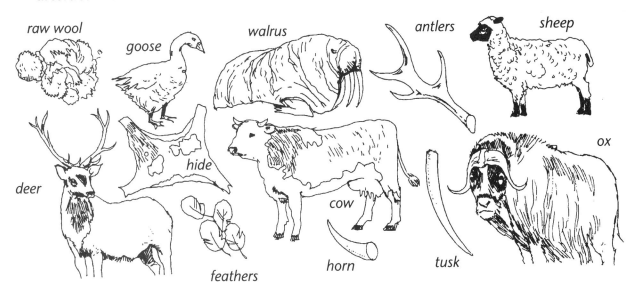

raw wool   goose   walrus   antlers   sheep

deer   hide   cow   ox

feathers   horn   tusk

Artefact	Raw material	Animal
Drinking horn		
Soft mattress		
Woollen cloak		
Ivory chess piece		
Leather shoes		
Comb		

- Suggest one other artefact that could be made from a part of each animal.
- Which of the artefacts do you think would have been most useful to the Vikings? Why?
- How do you think historians know about artefacts like this? Think carefully about what the artefacts were made from.
- Write a list of what we use today instead of these artefacts, and what they might be made from.

Sacrifice

In the year 922 an Arab visitor in Russia, Ibn Fadlan, met a Viking tribe called the Rus. He wrote down what happened when they burned the body of their chief in a longship.

The great chief had died. His body was put on a couch, in a tent, on his longship. This had been pulled on to the shore near the river. His family asked his slaves, "Who will die with him?" A girl answered, "I will. I see my master sitting in Paradise. Let me go to him."

Now a fat and strong old woman arrived. She looked grim and the Rus called her the Angel of Death. The old woman took the girl and laid her by the side of the chief. She looped a cord around her neck and ordered two men to pull on the ends to strangle her. Finally the Angel of Death came forward with a broad-bladed dagger and stabbed the young slave between the ribs. Outside other men stood by, beating their shields with sticks to drown her cries.

Soon the chief's closest relative moved forward. He was naked. Holding a flaming torch he set fire to the wood under the ship. Quickly the flames raced across the deck. A Rus next to me said, 'You Arabs are stupid. You take the people you love most and bury them in the ground for the worms. We burn them and in the twinkling of an eye they are in paradise.'

- Why do you think the girl was ready to die with her master?

- What does the story tell you about the Angel of Death? Use this to help you draw a picture of her.

- Why did the Rus say Ibn was stupid?

- Do you think this kind of thing still happens today? Explain your answer.
- If you had been standing beside Ibn watching the Viking sacrifice, what would you have thought of the Vikings?

Names

I'll call you ...

Viking warriors and kings liked to give each other nicknames. These were usually based on how they looked, something they owned or something they were good at.

● Read this list of famous Vikings. Why do think they were called these names?

Name	My reason
Eric Blood-Axe	
Harald Blue-Tooth	
Harald Red-Beard	
Helgi the Lean	
Ragnar Hairy Breek (trousers)	
Sigtrygg One-Eye	

● Look at these Vikings. What nickname would you give them?

● Choose five of your friends and give them Viking-style nicknames. Don't be rude!

Crime and punishment

The Vikings had no police and no prisons. People found guilty of serious crimes could be hanged, or have their foot or hand cut off.

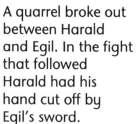 

A quarrel broke out between Harald and Egil. In the fight that followed Harald had his hand cut off by Egil's sword.

Punishment: _____

Weregild

If you hurt or killed someone you had to pay money to that person or their family. If you killed a nobleman you had to pay 1200 shillings, but for a slave only 200 shillings. Stealing things or hurting someone also had their own prices. The money paid was known as weregild.

Karl has been found guilty of stealing silver spoons from his master. He has stolen things before.

Punishment: _____

King Sven has to punish several people for crimes. He asks your advice.

● Make the punishment fit the crime. Explain why you have chosen these punishments.

Thrall has run away from his master but has been caught. He has run away twice before.

Punishment: _____

● How do you think each of these crimes would be punished today? Explain your answer.
● Make up your own cases to be judged. Ask your partner how they should be punished.

In memory

Some Vikings set up stones to remember their dead relatives. Sometimes these were in memory of people who had died far away from home and whose bodies had not been recovered. These are called memorial stones. They had writing and pictures on them.

This is a memorial stone to Harald Blue-Tooth.

● Look carefully at the carving of the man – he is on a cross.
  Why might Harald have this picture on his memorial stone?

King Cnut was a famous Viking leader. He was a very fierce warrior who ruled Norway, Denmark and England. He was also a Christian king who gave money to help build churches.

● Using the information, draw a memorial stone for King Cnut in the box. Remember the Vikings liked to carve twisted patterns on stones like dragons or snakes. You could also add some writing to your stone.

● Why do you think the Vikings felt it was important to have memorial stones?
● Do people still have stones like this today? In what way?

Runes

The Vikings had a different alphabet from ours. Their letters were called runes and were often carved into wood or stone. Because of this they had very few rounded letters, as they would have been difficult to carve.

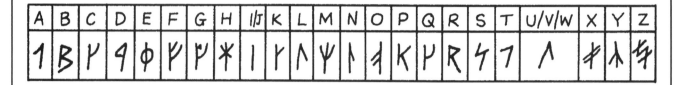

A	B	C	D	E	F	G	H	I/J	K	L	M	N	O	P	Q	R	S	T	U/V/W	X	Y	Z
↑	B	Y	٩	Φ	Ⴌ	Ⴊ	⋇	I	Γ	Λ	Ψ	٦	٤	K	Ⴒ	R	Ϟ	↑	Λ	⋕	⋏	⋕⋕

This is a signpost to the town of Yorvik. On the signpost are the names of different traders and craftspeople.

- Use the table to find out what each name means. Draw a trail to the correct craftsperson.

- What does this signpost tell us about the lifestyle of the Vikings?

- One name is missing. What is it? Write the name in runes.

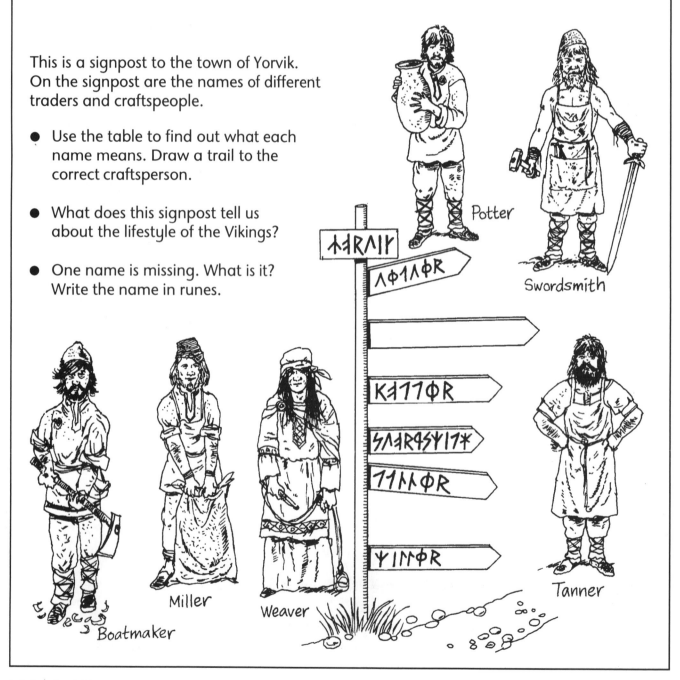

Potter

Swordsmith

Boatmaker

Miller

Weaver

Tanner

Who goes where?

In Viking society, some people were thought important and others not important at all. Below is a poem called the *Rigspula*. Three people are described in the poem.

● Link each person to the correct picture.
  Look up any words you are not sure of.

The first person is called Thrall.

Rough were his hands
With wrinkled skin
With knuckles knotty
With fingers thick
His face was ugly
His back was humpy

The second person is called Earl.

Blond his hair and bright his cheeks
Eyes as fierce as a young snake
Earl grew up in that same hall
To throw a spear and fire a bow
Ride on horseback and hunt with dogs
Fight with a sword and swim like a fish

The third person is called Karl.

Working oxen, making ploughs,
Building houses, building barns

The fourth person is not in the *Rigspula*.
● Write four lines for this person.

_____

_____

_____

_____

● Choose one of these headings to write below each picture.
● Who is the most important person?
● Who is the least important? Why?

Noble
Slave
Farmer
Servant

Heroes

This is a description of a Viking hero. Read through it carefully and underline all the words you think make this person a hero. This type of hero was called a *Beserker*.

> *The beserker was sitting on his horse wearing his helmet. He carried a leather shield with a rim of iron. He looked very frightening. He began to howl and bite the rim of his shield. He held the shield up to his mouth and made his eyes roll in his head like a madman.*

- What made this Viking frightening?
- Why would he want to look frightening?
- The Vikings thought of beserkers as heroes. Do you think a person like this would be a hero today? Why?

- Who do you think of as a hero? Draw a picture of your hero.

- Why do you think of this person as a hero?

- Is there a difference between your hero and the Viking hero? What is the difference? Why is there a difference?

Making Thor's hammer

Thor was one of the most popular Viking gods. Vikings believed you could hear him coming when the sky went black and boomed with thunder. The thunder was caused by Thor pulling his goat-drawn chariot across the sky.

Thor used a hammer in battle. Small copies of it were made as lucky charms, called 'amulets'. The Vikings believed these amulets would protect them from evil creatures.

- Follow these instructions to make Thor's amulet.

1. Cut a piece of modelling clay in two halves.

2. On the smooth sides of the two halves, carve an outline of Thor's hammer, then cut out the clay to form a mould. The two halves should be designed to fit together.

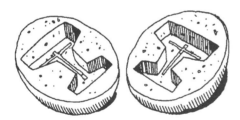

3. Place the two halves together, securing them tightly with an elastic band so that they will not come apart.

4. Bore a small hole in the top of the mould.

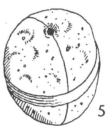

5. Pour liquid clay into the mould and leave to harden for at least 24 hours.

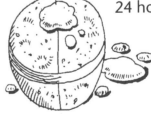

6. Break open the mould and you will have Thor's amulet!

- Write a list of some of the lucky charms people carry today. Choose one of them and explain why people think it is lucky.
- Find out more about Thor and write a description of him.

Advice from Odin

The sentences written below are wise sayings. They are taken from a Viking poem written about AD850, called *The Words of the High One*. They were so full of good advice that people believed they were first spoken by Odin, the leading god.

Look carefully round doorways before you walk in: there might be an enemy hiding.

Never leave your weapons when you go out into the fields; you never know when you might need them.

Only tell your secrets to one person, never two. Tell three and the whole world will know.

There is no better load a person can carry than common sense; no worse load than too much drink.

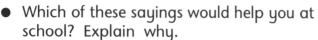

Don't say good things about the day until evening, about your wife until she is buried, about a sword until it has been used, about a sheet of ice until you have crossed it, about beer until you have drunk it.

- Which of these sayings would help you at school? Explain why.
- Make up a wise saying to help these people.

Asa is worried about choosing the right kind of husband.

Advice to Asa

_____

_____

_____

Harald is looking for somewhere to hide his silver coins so they will not be stolen.

Advice to Harold

_____

_____

_____

- We call wise sayings proverbs. Write down five proverbs we use today.

Reading the stones

The Vikings left many fine carved stones that tell us about their beliefs. This picture shows a side of a carving called the Ragnarok Stone found on the Isle of Man. Ragnarok was a Viking word meaning 'the end of the world'.

- Find these scenes and sketch and label each one:
  1. Odin, the greatest Viking god, fighting for his life.
  2. Fenrir the wolf trying to kill him.
  3. The raven, Odin's holy bird.
  4. The shape of the cross.

- What does the stone tell us about Viking religion?

 ● Using reference books find out what you can about Odin and Ragnarok. Look out for the Frost Giants at the end of the world. Who are they?

Odin, the greatest Viking god.

Burial

Vikings buried their dead along with many objects they used during their lives. Archaeologists dig up these burials for clues about the Viking way of life. Help Professor Thor to fill in his archaeological report.

- How many people are buried here?

  _____

- What sort of person was this? (A farmer, a merchant, a warrior?)

  _____

- How might this Viking have travelled around?

  _____

- Why could he not have been buried before AD930?

  _____

- What does this burial site tell us about Viking beliefs about death?

  _____

KEY
1. Metal bosses (centres of shields)
2. Spearheads   3. Comb
4. Stirrups   5. Bowl
6. Axe   7. Knife
8. Sword   9. Arrowheads
10. The body
11. Arabic Coin (made about A.D.930)

 • Draw how you think this person would have looked.

Digging up the Vikings

We know a lot about Viking life because of remains that have been carefully dug from the ground by archaeologists. Often the things they find are damaged or broken.

- An archaeologist has found this iron helmet. Help her to put it back together.

- Cut out the pieces and glue them together on another sheet of paper. Draw in the missing parts to show what the whole helmet looked like.

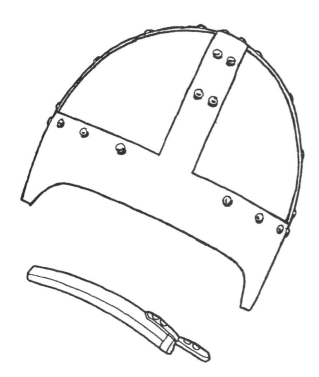

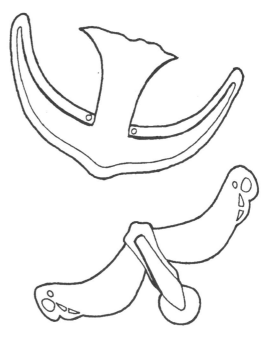

- Suggest why a Viking would wear a helmet like this. What does it tell us about the Vikings?

- Why do you think it is sometimes difficult for archaeologists to put items back together? What other evidence could they use to help them?

- Write a list of items we use today that would help archaeologists in the future understand our way of life.

BRAIN WAVES – *Vikings*

Festival

Vikings from Norway settled in the north of Scotland in AD850. Today the people of the Shetland Islands are still proud of their Viking ancestors. They hold a Viking fire festival every January called Up-Helly-Aa.

● Read the song carefully and use a dictionary to find the meanings of any words you do not know.

This picture shows the highpoint of Up-Helly-Ha – burning a Viking ship.

Grand old Vikings ruled the ocean vast,
Their brave battle songs still thunder on the blast,
Their wild war-cry comes a-ringing from the past,
We answer it "A-oi!"
Roll their glory down the ages,
Son of warriors and sages,
Where the fight for freedom rages,
Be bold and strong as they!

● How do you know this is a Viking festival?
● How do you know this festival is taking place in modern times?
● What use might this festival be to Shetlanders today?

● What would you include in a Viking festival at your school?
● Imagine you work for a newspaper and have been sent to report on Up-Helly-Aa. Write a report about the festival, telling your readers what is happening.

Viking English

Anglo-Saxons and Vikings could talk to each other because their languages were similar. Some Anglo-Saxon and Viking words meant nearly the same thing. After a time most people spoke English, but with many Viking words added to the language.

● Use a dictionary to fill in the table. Find out which language each pair of words is from.

		Viking or Old Norse	Anglo-Saxon or Old English
rear	raise		
wish	want		
skill	craft		
hide	skin		
scant	short		

● Write down what each word means. How is it similar to the other word in the pair? How is it different?

	Meaning	Similar	Different
rear			
raise			
wish			
want			
skill			
craft			
hide			
skin			
scant			
short			

● There are at least 1000 Viking or Old Norse words in modern English. Use a dictionary to list as many as you can. Try looking up words beginning with 'sk'.

The Vikings settled here

When the Vikings settled in England they often lived close to the Anglo-Saxons who were already there. We can find evidence for this by studying the ends of place names still used today.

- Look carefully at this map of the coast of Lincolnshire. Using the place name tables to help you, underline Viking settlements in red and Anglo-Saxon settlements in blue.

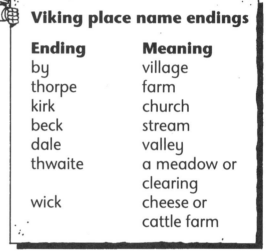

Viking place name endings

Ending	Meaning
by	village
thorpe	farm
kirk	church
beck	stream
dale	valley
thwaite	a meadow or clearing
wick	cheese or cattle farm

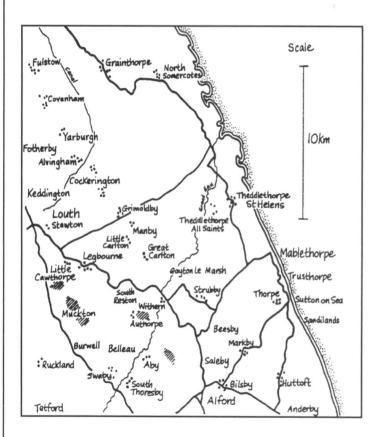

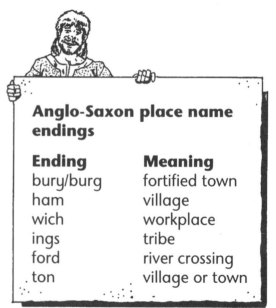

Anglo-Saxon place name endings

Ending	Meaning
bury/burg	fortified town
ham	village
wich	workplace
ings	tribe
ford	river crossing
ton	village or town

- Look at a map of your home area. Make a list of any Viking or Anglo-Saxon names you can find.
- Was your home area mainly Anglo-Saxon or Viking? It may have been neither.

BRAIN WAVES – Vikings